30.4
days ot
~~nonsense~~

illustrating Edward Lear verses

30.5 days of nonsense illustrating Edward Lear verses

ISBN: 978-1-7393610-9-9 paperback

Publisher: Z-proof Editorial Services
Cover design and editing: Z-proof Editorial Services
https://zproofeditorial.wordpress.com/

Original verses by Edward Lear, first published 1846, now in the public
domain
Cover illustration generated using DALL E

~~Contents~~

List of (predominantly) old (and a few young) sods

(Do you know all the places that Lear references?)

a brilliant introduction

Edward Lear's *A Book of Nonsense* was first published in 1846. It comprises over 100 limericks, types of poems that have a rhyming pattern of AABBA. Lear's limericks all tell funny (well, they were extremely funny at a time of no films or cartoons, and some of them still invoke mirth) tales about specific individuals. This book pays homage to Lear and allows you, yes YOU, to illustrate his verses.

Apart from being a writer (and a musician) Lear (1812-1888) was also an illustrator. He was initially an illustrator of birds, but he went on to illustrate his own stories and poems with not just birds but all sorts of animals and people-like people.

Now, I've removed the verses that might attract criticism in the present day, such as the one with the Old Man of Jamaica (although I wonder if Lear was actually taking an anti-racist stance with that verse, which if so, might have been one of the first such stances in English literature) and those with mention of exaggerated facial features, such as an Old Man with a Nose. I've also cut those that could prompt grisly drawings such as The Old Man of the Nile or the Old Man of Whitehaven. The Old Man in a Boat also didn't seem suitable, and domestic abuse and animal cruelty were axed. It is important to keep in mind that Lear's works were written in the Victorian age, a time when published literature was largely created by educated White male writers who had a rather singular of the world. Thankfully that nonsense is changing.

So, be Lear-like, and draw something funny that matches each verse. There's a verse for each day of the month (assuming you're not drawing in a month that has 28, 29, 30, or 32 days).

How to draw nonsense

Just draw!

Start by drawing basic shapes for the body, such as a circle for a head. Then, you can add details.

Add lines to suggest movement and shadows.

There was a Young Lady of Clare,
Who was madly pursued by a bear;
When she found she was tired, she abruptly expired,
That unfortunate Lady of Clare.

This is how Lear drew it. That bear is pretty big, isn't it?

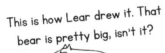
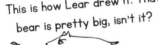

Stick figures make for cool bods, too.

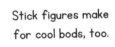

Be as silly as you want.

Draw bold black lines, or soft feathery strokes.

There was an Old Person of Dover,
Who rushed through a field of blue
clover;
But some very large Bees stung his nose
and his knees,
So he very soon went back to Dover.

There was an Old Lady of Chertsey,
Who made a remarkable curtsey;
She twirled round and round, till she
sank underground,
Which distressed all the people of
Chertsey.

There was an Old Person of Chili,
Whose conduct was painful and silly;
He sate on the stairs, eating apples and pears,
That imprudent Old Person of Chili.

There was an Old Man of Moldavia,
Who had the most curious behavior;
For while he was able, he slept on a
table,
That funny Old Man of Moldavia.

There was an Old Man of the Isles,
Whose face was pervaded with smiles;
He sang "High dum diddle," and played on
the fiddle,
That amiable Man of the Isles.

There was an Old Man of Quebec,—
A beetle ran over his neck;
But he cried, "With a needle I'll slay you,
O beadle!"
That angry Old Man of Quebec.

There was an Old Person whose habits
Induced him to feed upon Rabbits;
When he'd eaten eighteen, he turned
perfectly green,
Upon which he relinquished those habits.

There was an Old Person of Mold,
Who shrank from sensations of cold;
So he purchased some muffs, some furs,
and some fluffs,
And wrapped himself well from the cold.

There was an Old Man of Dundee,
Who frequented the top of a tree;
When disturbed by the Crows, he abruptly arose,
And exclaimed, "I'll return to Dundee!"

There was an Old Lady whose folly
Induced her to sit in a holly;
Whereon, by a thorn her dress being
torn,
She quickly became melancholy.

There was a Young Lady of Troy,
Whom several large flies did annoy;
Some she Killed with a thump, some she
drowned at the pump,
And some she tooK with her to Troy.

There was a Young Lady of Hull,
Who was chased by a virulent Bull;
But she seized on a spade, and called
out, "Who's afraid?"
Which distracted that virulent Bull.

There was an Old Man of Aôsta
Who possessed a large Cow, but he lost
her;
But they said, "Don't you see she has
run up a tree,
You invidious Old Man of Aôsta?"

There was a Young Person of Crete,
Whose toilette was far from complete;
She dressed in a sack spickle-speckled
with black,
That ombliferous Person of Crete.

There was a Young Lady of DorKing,
Who bought a large bonnet for walKing;
But its color and size so bedazzled her
eyes,
That she very soon went bacK to
DorKing.

There was an Old Man of Peru.
Who never Knew what he should do;
So he tore off his hair, and behaved like
a bear,
That intrinsic Old Man of Peru.

There was an Old Man with a beard,
Who said, "It is just as I feared!—
Two Owls and a Hen, four Larks and a
Wren,
Have all built their nests in my beard."

There was an Old Man of Nepaul,
From his horse had a terrible fall;
But, though split quite in two, with some
very strong glue
They mended that man of Nepaul.

There was a Young Lady of Russia,
Who screamed so that no one could
hush her;
Her screams were extreme,—no one
heard such a scream
As was screamed by that Lady of Russia.

There was a Young Lady of Ryde,
Whose shoe-strings were seldom untied;
She purchased some clogs, and some
small spotty Dogs,
And frequently walked about Ryde.

There was an Old Person of Gretna,
Who rushed down the crater of Etna;
When they said, "Is it hot?" he replied,
"No, it's not!"
That mendacious Old Person of Gretna.

There was an Old Man of the West,
Who never could get any rest;
So they set him to spin on his nose and
his chin,
Which cured that Old Man of the West.

There was an Old Person of Sparta,
Who had twenty-five sons and one
"darter;"
He fed them on Snails, and weighed
them in scales,
That wonderful Person of Sparta.

There was an Old Man of Coblenz,
The length of whose legs was immense;
He went with one prance from Turkey
to France,
That surprising Old Man of Coblenz.

There was an Old Man of Melrose,
Who walked on the tips of his toes;
But they said, "It ain't pleasant to see
you at present,
You stupid Old Man of Melrose."

There was an Old Person of Tring,
Who embellished his nose with a ring;
He gazed at the moon every evening in
June,
That ecstatic Old Person of Tring.

There was an Old Man of the South,
Who had an immoderate mouth;
But in swallowing a dish that was quite
full of Fish,
He was choked, that Old Man of the
South.

There was an Old Person of Anerley,
Whose conduct was strange and
unmannerly;
He rushed down the Strand with a Pig in
each hand,
But returned in the evening to Anerley.

There was a Young Lady of Norway,
Who casually sat in a doorway;
When the door squeezed her flat, she
exclaimed, "What of that?"
This courageous Young Lady of Norway.

There was a Young Lady of Turkey,
Who wept when the weather was murky;
When the day turned out fine, she
ceased to repine,
That capricious Young Lady of Turkey.

day 30.5

There was an Old Man who said, "How Shall I flee from this horrible Cow?
I will sit on this stile, and continue to smile,
Which may soften the heart of that Cow."

Compose your own nonsense

any day

There was . . .

Titles by Z Smith available on Amazon KDP

Printed in Great Britain
by Amazon

37076771R00030